Catch-Up 2020 Revision pack

Pearson Edexcel GCSE (9–1) Mathematics
Foundation tier

Includes

Knowledge check diagnostic self-test

Revision Guide + App

and

Revision Workbook

Get back on track

The COVID-19 pandemic has been disruptive for students of all ages around the world. And if you're preparing for your GCSEs then it's especially important that you catch up on any work you've missed. This pack is designed to help you revise and practise any topics you might need a reminder on, and stay on track for success in your Pearson Edexcel Mathematics GCSE course.

Time for a check-up

Take the **Knowledge check** diagnostic self-test to help you identify which topics and skills you need to recap. The questions in this test focus on key skills and core knowledge that you will need to know to succeed in the rest of your GCSE course, and in your exams.

You can mark your own work using the **answers** on the back cover (page 20) of this booklet. If you struggle with any of the questions, just add the Revision Guide page numbers for that question to your custom catch-up plan on page 15. Then you can revise and practise that topic and build your confidence.

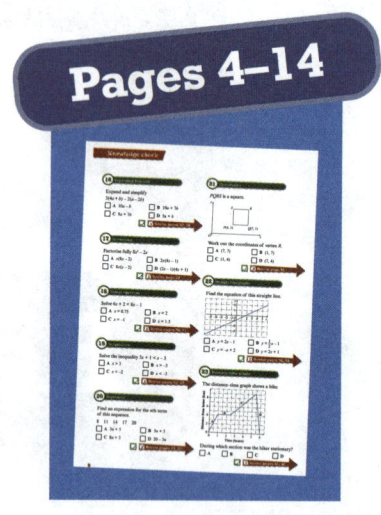

Pages 4–14

Make a plan

Create your own custom **Catch-up plan** by entering the page numbers you need to revise in the table on page 15. You can use the tick boxes to track your progress, and there is space on pages 16 and 17 to add any extra notes from your teacher or tutor.

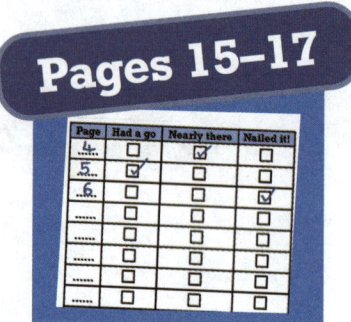

Pages 15–17

Stress-free studying

Here are a few top tips from our experts to stay healthy and sane when things get busy!

- Set yourself simple targets, like reviewing a couple of pages of the Revision Guide in a 20-minute study session.
- Phone a friend! If you're struggling with a topic, ask one of your friends if they've figured it out and can explain it to you.
- Find a quiet space at home or at school – use headphones if it helps you to concentrate.
- Put your phone on silent, and try not to get distracted by TV or the internet.
- Drink plenty of water, get plenty of sleep, take breaks and stay active!

GCSE MATHEMATICS FOUNDATION CATCH-UP 2020

Once you have identified your target topics and created your catch-up plan, it's time to break open the books and get revising. The Revision Guide and Revision Workbook in your pack have matching page numbers to help you find your way around quickly and easily.

Your **Revision Guide** is packed with essential facts, key skills and worked examples to help you stay ahead of the game. Each page covers a single topic so you can stay organised, and the book covers your **whole course**, so once you're back up to speed you will be able to use it alongside your school work, and to revise for your exams.

Check that you have nailed each topic by practising some exam-style questions on the corresponding page in the **Revision Workbook**. There are **guided questions** which give you part of the working, and hints and tips to help you get started. And when the exams are a bit closer, you can use the **exam-style practice papers** to check that you are exam-ready.

Find your catch-up topics

If you know which units or topics you want to revise, you can use the **Matching chart** to find the corresponding Revision Guide and Workbook pages. Your teacher or tutor might be able to tell you which units or topics you missed, or you might recognise them from the work you did at home during lockdown.

Tick the units or topics you want to revise, then add those page numbers to your catch-up plan on page 15.

Pages 18–19

Knowledge check

You can use the diagnostic self-test on the next 11 pages to help you create your own customised catch-up plan. Each question checks a different key skill or piece of core knowledge from your GCSE course. If you feel that you need more help with that topic or skill, add the page numbers shown in the arrows to your catch-up plan.

A bit at a time

There are 70 questions in this knowledge check. Have a go at them in chunks. When you have done a batch of 10 or 20 questions, check your answers on the back cover (page 20) of this booklet. Then take a break or come back and try some more in another study session!

Number

1 Place value

Write the number twelve thousand and thirty-one in figures.
- A 1231
- B 12031
- C 120031
- D 1200031

☑ ☒ Revise page 1

2 Negative numbers

Work out −4 + 6 × 2.
Do not use a calculator.
- A 8
- B 4
- C −16
- D −20

☑ ☒ Revise pages 2, 16

3 Rounding

Round 8.6592 to 1 significant figure.
- A 10
- B 8.7
- C 8.6
- D 9

☑ ☒ Revise pages 3, 10

4 Calculations with whole numbers

Work out 45 × 17
Do not use a calculator.
- A 918
- B 680
- C 360
- D 765

☑ ☒ Revise pages 4, 5

5 Calculations with decimals

Work out 0.49 + 1.3
Do not use a calculator.
- A 6.2
- B 1.79
- C 1.52
- D 1.349

☑ ☒ Revise pages 6, 7

6 Squares and cubes

Work out $3 + 12^2$.
Do not use a calculator.
- A 147
- B 169
- C 7
- D 49

☑ ☒ Revise pages 8, 16

GCSE MATHEMATICS FOUNDATION CATCH-UP 2020

7 Indices

Write $\dfrac{7^{10} \times 7^3}{7}$ as a single power of 7.

- A 7^{29}
- B 7^{12}
- C 7^{23}
- D 7^{-13}

Revise page 9

8 Factors and primes

Express 600 as a product of its prime factors.

- A $2^2 \times 5^2 \times 6$
- B $2^3 \times 3^2 \times 5^3$
- C $2^3 \times 3 \times 5^2$
- D $2 \times 3 \times 10^2$

Revise pages 11, 12

9 Fractions

Work out $\dfrac{4}{5}$ of £60. Do not use a calculator.

- A £75
- B £12
- C £48
- D £45

Revise pages 13, 14

10 Rounding

Work out $1\dfrac{7}{8} \times 3\dfrac{2}{5}$

- A $6\dfrac{3}{8}$
- B $4\dfrac{9}{13}$
- C $3\dfrac{7}{20}$
- D $5\dfrac{1}{8}$

Revise page 15

11 Standard form

Write 736 000 in standard form.

- A 7.36×10^3
- B 736×10^3
- C 7.36×10^5
- D 7.36×10^{-6}

Revise pages 17, 18

Algebra

12 Collecting like terms

Simplify $3x - 2y + 5x - y$

- A $8x - 3y$
- B $8x - 2$
- C $x + 4y$
- D $2x + 3y$

Revise page 22

13 Simplifying terms

Simplify $3n \times 2n \times z$

- A $5nz$
- B $6nz$
- C $5n^2z$
- D $6n^2z$

Revise page 23

14 Algebraic indices

Simplify $(x^2y)^3$

- A x^2y^3
- B x^5y^3
- C xy^6
- D x^6y^3

Revise page 24

15 Formulae

$P = 5Q^2 - 2QR$

Find the value of P when $Q = 4$ and $R = -3$

- A 76
- B 104
- C 112
- D 56

Revise pages 26, 27

Knowledge check

16 Expanding brackets

Expand and simplify
$3(4a + b) - 2(a - 2b)$

- A $10a - b$
- B $10a + 7b$
- C $9a + 7b$
- D $5a + b$

✓ ✗ Revise pages 22, 28

17 Factorising

Factorise fully $8x^2 - 2x$

- A $x(8x - 2)$
- B $2x(4x - 1)$
- C $8x(x - 2)$
- D $(2x - 1)(4x + 1)$

✓ ✗ Revise page 29

18 Linear equations

Solve $6x + 2 = 8x - 1$

- A $x = 0.75$
- B $x = 2$
- C $x = -1$
- D $x = 1.5$

✓ ✗ Revise pages 30, 31

19 Inequalities

Solve the inequality $3x + 1 < x - 5$

- A $x > 3$
- B $x > -3$
- C $x < -2$
- D $x < -3$

✓ ✗ Revise pages 32, 33

20 Sequences

Find an expression for the nth term of this sequence.

8   11   14   17   20

- A $3n + 5$
- B $5n + 3$
- C $8n + 3$
- D $20 - 3n$

✓ ✗ Revise pages 34, 35

21 Coordinates

$PQRS$ is a square.

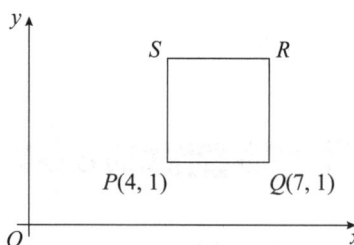

Work out the coordinates of vertex R.

- A $(7, 7)$
- B $(1, 7)$
- C $(1, 4)$
- D $(7, 4)$

✓ ✗ Revise page 36

22 Straight line graphs

Find the equation of this straight line.

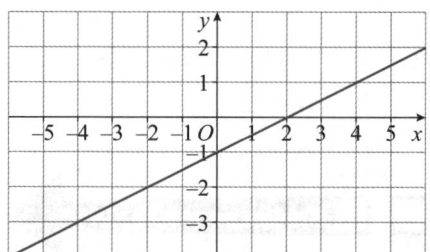

- A $y = 2x - 1$
- B $y = \frac{1}{2}x - 1$
- C $y = -x + 2$
- D $y = 2x + 1$

✓ ✗ Revise pages 38, 39

23 Distance–time graphs

The distance–time graph shows a hike.

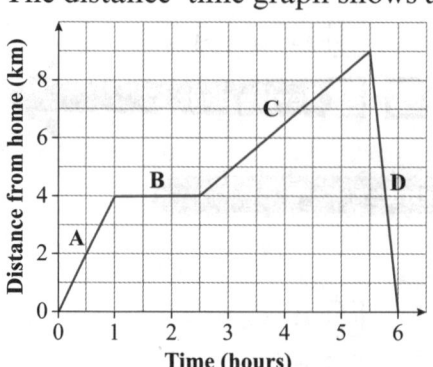

During which section was the hiker stationary?

- A
- B
- C
- D

✓ ✗ Revise pages 41, 42

24 Velocity–time graphs

The velocity–time graph shows the velocity of a runner.

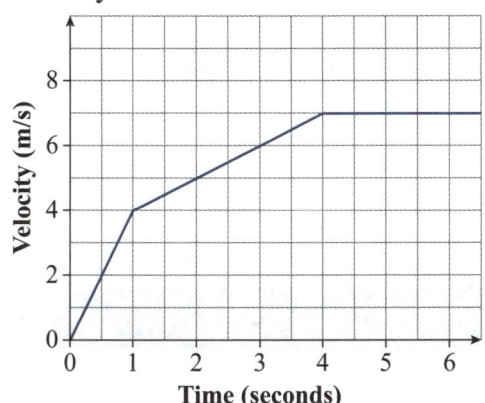

Which **one** of the following statements is **not** true?

- [ ] **A** The runner was moving fastest for the first second of the race
- [ ] **B** The runner was accelerating for the first second of the race
- [ ] **C** The runner was travelling at a constant speed between 4 and 6 seconds
- [ ] **D** The runner reached a speed of 7 m/s after 4 seconds

Revise page 42

25 Double brackets

Expand and simplify $(2x + 3)^2$

- [ ] **A** $4x^2 + 9$
- [ ] **B** $2x^2 + 6x + 9$
- [ ] **C** $4x^2 + 12x + 9$
- [ ] **D** $4x^2 + 6x + 9$

Revise page 43

26 Quadratic graphs

Match this graph to the correct equation.

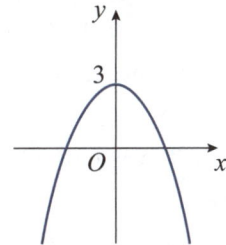

- [ ] **A** $y = 3 - x^2$
- [ ] **B** $y = x^2 - 3$
- [ ] **C** $y = x^2 + 3$
- [ ] **D** $y = x^3$

Revise pages 44, 45, 48

27 Factorising quadratics

Factorise $x^2 - 4x - 12$

- [ ] **A** $4x(x - 3)$
- [ ] **B** $(x - 4)(x + 3)$
- [ ] **C** $(x - 6)(x + 2)$
- [ ] **D** $(x - 4)^2$

Revise page 46

28 Quadratic equations

Solve the equation $x^2 - 10x + 16 = 0$

- [ ] **A** $x = 1.6$
- [ ] **B** $x = -4$
- [ ] **C** $x = 8$ or $x = 2$
- [ ] **D** $x = -8$ or $x = -2$

Revise page 47

29 Simultaneous equations

Solve the simultaneous equations

$5x + 6y = 5$
$x - 2y = 9$

- [ ] **A** $x = -3, y = 1.5$
- [ ] **B** $x = 4, y = -2.5$
- [ ] **C** $x = 2.5, y = 5$
- [ ] **D** $x = -3, y = -1.5$

Revise page 49

30 Rearranging formulae

$M = 6R - 20$

Rearrange the formula to make R the subject.

- [ ] **A** $R = \dfrac{M + 20}{6}$
- [ ] **B** $R = 6M + 20$
- [ ] **C** $R = \dfrac{M}{6} + 20$
- [ ] **D** $R = \dfrac{1}{6}(M - 20)$

Revise page 50

Knowledge check

31 Proof

n is an integer.
Which of the following is an even number?

- A $(n+1)(n-1)$
- B $2n-1$
- C $(n+1)^2$
- D $(n+1)+(n-1)$

Revise pages 51, 52

Ratio and proportion

32 Percentages

Work out 15% of £900.

- A £145
- B £1035
- C £135
- D £180

Revise pages 55, 56

33 Percentage change

Jacob's luggage weighs 25 kg.
He reduces the weight of his luggage by 12%.
What is the new weight of Jacob's luggage?

- A 20 kg
- B 13 kg
- C 22 kg
- D 3 kg

Revise pages 57, 58

34 Ratio

The ratio of juice to water in a drink is 3:2
The total amount of drink is 600 ml.
How much juice is in the drink?

- A 200 ml
- B 360 ml
- C 400 ml
- D 450 ml

Revise pages 59, 60

35 Converting units

Convert 2.8 km into metres.

- A 2800 m
- B 280 m
- C 28 m
- D 0.28 m

Revise page 61

36 Reverse percentage change

In a sale, prices are reduced by 20%.
The sale price of a phone is £144.
Work out its original price.

- A £180
- B £172.80
- C £192
- D £115.20

Revise page 62

37 Exponential growth

Alison invests £800 in a savings account, which pays 2.5% compound interest.
Work out the amount Alison has in her account after 4 years.
Give your answer to the nearest pound.

- A £883
- B £861
- C £1953
- D £880

Revise page 63

GCSE MATHEMATICS FOUNDATION CATCH-UP 2020

38 Speed

A cyclist travels 84 km at an average speed of 15 km/h.

Work out the total time taken.

- [ ] A 4.5 hours
- [ ] B 0.18 hours
- [ ] C 1260 hours
- [ ] D 5.6 hours

Revise page 64

39 Density and compound measures

A brass ornament has a volume of 120 cm³. The density of brass is 8.6 g/cm³.

Work out the mass of the ornament.

- [ ] A 14.0 g
- [ ] B 0.07 g
- [ ] C 516 g
- [ ] D 1032 g

Revise pages 65, 66

40 Proportion

It takes 6 workers a total of 12 days to build a wall.

How long would it take 4 workers to build the same wall, if they worked at the same rate?

- [ ] A 8 days
- [ ] B 16 days
- [ ] C 18 days
- [ ] D 24 days

Revise pages 67, 68

Geometry and measures

41 2D shapes

Which of the following shapes can have **no** lines of symmetry?

- [ ] A rhombus
- [ ] B parallelogram
- [ ] C rectangle
- [ ] D kite

Revise pages 71, 72

42 Angle facts

Which one of the following is **not** a true angle fact?

- [ ] A Angles in a triangle add up to 180°
- [ ] B Angles on a straight line add up to 180°
- [ ] C Angles around a point add up to 180°
- [ ] D Vertically opposite angles are equal

Revise page 73

43 Angle properties

Work out the size of the angle marked x.

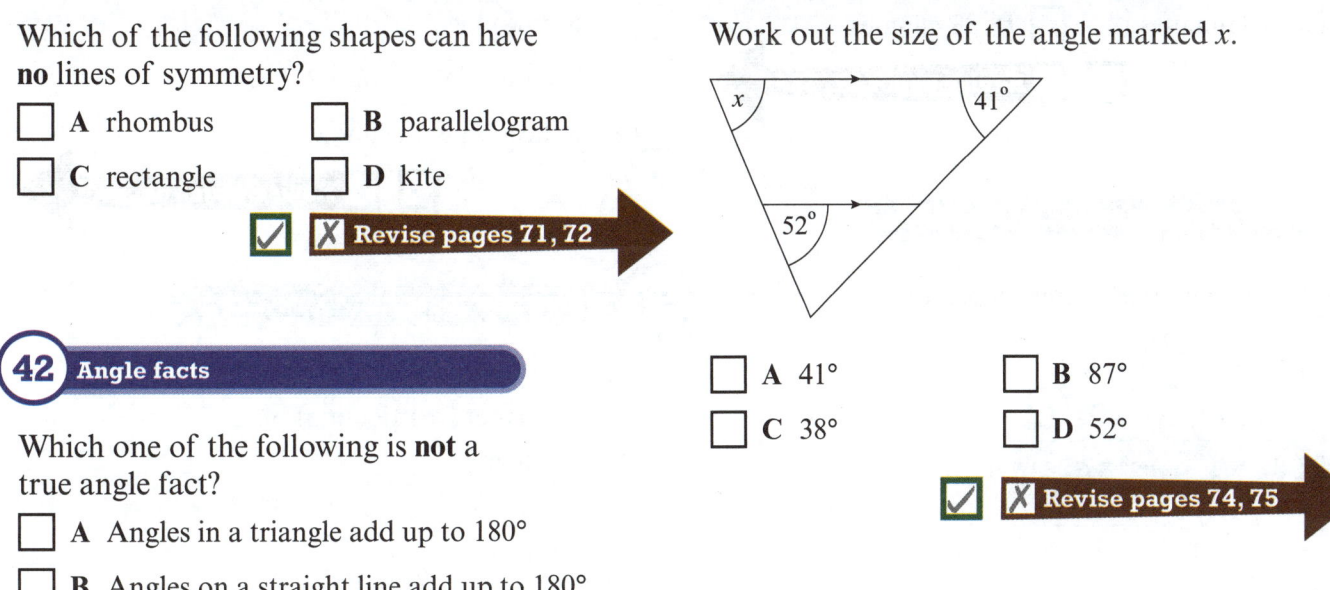

- [ ] A 41°
- [ ] B 87°
- [ ] C 38°
- [ ] D 52°

Revise pages 74, 75

Knowledge check

44 Angles in polygons

The diagram shows a regular octagon.
Work out the size of the angle marked x.

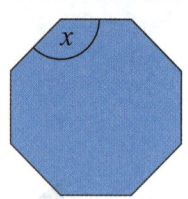

- [ ] **A** 135°
- [ ] **B** 45°
- [ ] **C** 145°
- [ ] **D** 315°

✓ ✗ Revise page 76

45 Measures

Here is part of a bus timetable.

Felixstowe	0920	0940
Heath Road	0950	1010
Ipswich	1008	1028

How long is the journey from Felixstowe to Ipswich?

- [ ] **A** 18 minutes
- [ ] **B** 30 minutes
- [ ] **C** 48 minutes
- [ ] **D** 38 minutes

✓ ✗ Revise pages 77, 78

46 Perimeter and area

Work out the area of this trapezium.

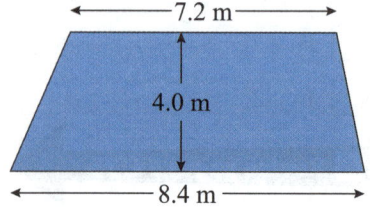

- [ ] **A** 33.6 m²
- [ ] **B** 62.4 m²
- [ ] **C** 31.2 m²
- [ ] **D** 37.2 m²

✓ ✗ Revise pages 79, 81

47 Volumes of 3D solids

Work out the volume of this cuboid.

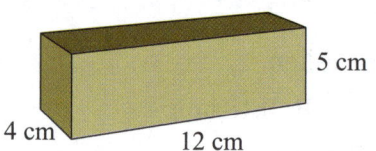

- [ ] **A** 48 cm²
- [ ] **B** 120 cm³
- [ ] **C** 240 cm³
- [ ] **D** 80 cm³

✓ ✗ Revise pages 82, 83

48 Transformations

Describe fully the single transformation that maps triangle **P** onto triangle **Q**.

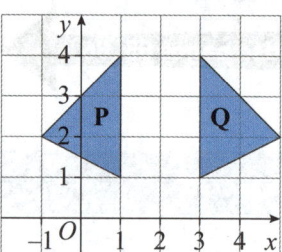

- [ ] **A** Reflection
- [ ] **B** Rotation
- [ ] **C** Rotation 180° about (2, 2.5)
- [ ] **D** Reflection in the line $x = 2$

✓ ✗ Revise pages 86, 88

49 Pythagoras' theorem

Work out the length of BC in this right-angled triangle, correct to 1 decimal place.

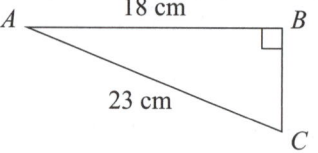

- [ ] **A** 5.0 cm
- [ ] **B** 14.3 cm
- [ ] **C** 29.2 cm
- [ ] **D** 205.0 cm

✓ ✗ Revise pages 90, 91

50 Trigonometry

Work out the size of the angle marked *x* in this right-angled triangle, to the nearest degree.

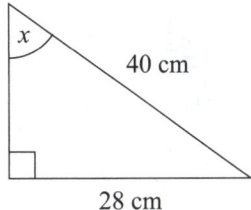

- [ ] **A** 55°
- [ ] **B** 35°
- [ ] **C** 46°
- [ ] **D** 44°

Revise pages 92, 94

51 Measuring

Measure this angle correct to the nearest degree.

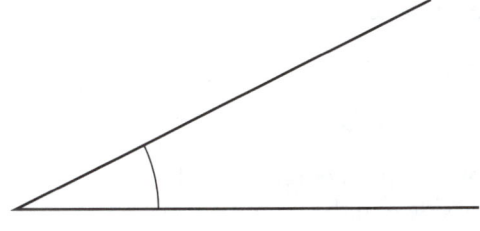

- [ ] **A** 26°
- [ ] **B** 27°
- [ ] **C** 154°
- [ ] **D** 155°

Revise pages 95, 96

52 Bearings

The bearing of point *P* from point *Q* is 208°. Find the bearing of point *Q* from point *P*.

- [ ] **A** 018°
- [ ] **B** 28°
- [ ] **C** 028°
- [ ] **D** 388°

Revise pages 98, 102

53 Loci and constructions

Which of the following describes the points in the shaded region?

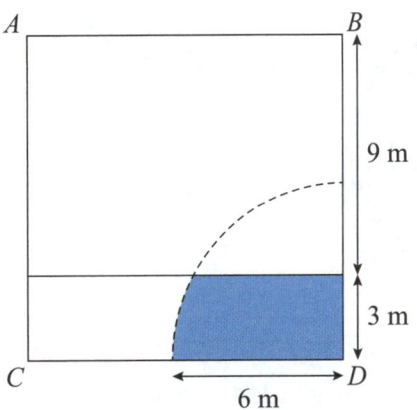

- [ ] **A** Closer to *D* than *A* and at least 9 m from *AB*
- [ ] **B** Less than 3 m from *CD* and less than 6 m from *D*
- [ ] **C** At least 9 m from *AB* and less than 6 m from *D*
- [ ] **D** Less than or equal to 6 m from *D* and less than 3 m from *CD*

Revise pages 99, 101

54 Areas of circles

A circle has a radius of 10 cm.
Work out the area of the circle.
Give your answer to 3 significant figures.

- [ ] **A** 31.4 cm²
- [ ] **B** 314 cm²
- [ ] **C** 78.5 cm²
- [ ] **D** 100 cm²

Revise pages 103, 104

Knowledge check

55 Sectors of circles

The diagram shows a circle with centre O and radius 5 cm.

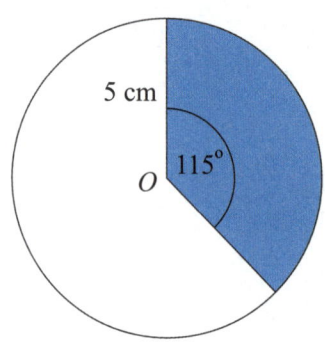

Work out the area of the shaded sector to 3 significant figures.

☐ A 26.2 cm²   ☐ B 7.98 cm²
☐ C 25.1 cm²   ☐ D 627 cm²

☑ ☒ Revise page 105

56 Cylinders

Work out the volume of this cylinder, to the nearest cm³.

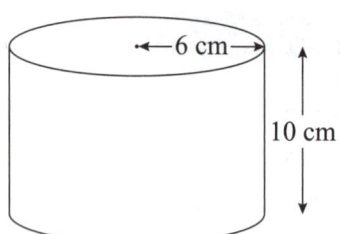

☐ A 377 cm³   ☐ B 1131 cm³
☐ C 360 cm³   ☐ D 1885 cm³

☑ ☒ Revise pages 106, 108

57 Similar shapes

The diagram shows two similar triangles.

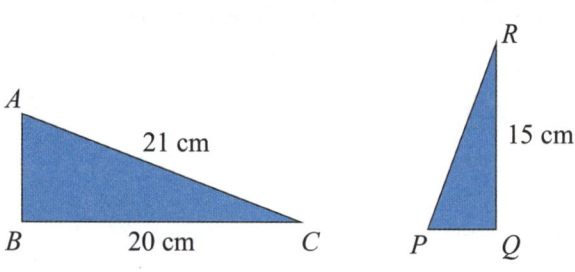

Find the length of side PR.

☐ A 18 cm   ☐ B 14.3 cm
☐ C 20 cm   ☐ D 15.75 cm

☑ ☒ Revise page 110

58 Congruency

Which of the following is **not** a condition of congruency for triangles?

☐ A All three angles equal
☐ B Two sides and the included angle equal
☐ C All three sides equal
☐ D Right-angle with hypotenuse and one other side equal

☑ ☒ Revise pages 109, 111

59 Vectors

$\mathbf{p} = \begin{pmatrix} -2 \\ 5 \end{pmatrix}$ and $\mathbf{q} = \begin{pmatrix} 3 \\ -3 \end{pmatrix}$

Work out the vector $\mathbf{p} - 2\mathbf{q}$

☐ A $\begin{pmatrix} 4 \\ -1 \end{pmatrix}$ ☐ B $\begin{pmatrix} -1 \\ 8 \end{pmatrix}$
☐ C $\begin{pmatrix} -4 \\ 8 \end{pmatrix}$ ☐ D $\begin{pmatrix} -8 \\ 11 \end{pmatrix}$

☑ ☒ Revise page 112

Statistics and probability

60 Two-way tables

This two-way table shows the male and female members of a class.

	Left-handed	Right-handed	Total
Girls	2	3	9
Boys		12	
Total	5	16	

How many boys were in the class in total?

- A 12
- B 15
- C 3
- D 27

✓ ✗ Revise page 115

61 Representing data

This pictogram shows the amounts of money raised by two students in a sponsored swim.

| Nicola | ◐ ◐ ◐ ◐ ◐ ◐ |
| Amir | ◐ ◐ ◐ ◐ |

Key: ◐ represents £10

How much did Nicola raise?

- A £55
- B £50
- C £60
- D £110

✓ ✗ Revise pages 116, 117

62 Pie charts

A group of 100 students were asked their favourite colour.
Bertie draws a pie chart to show the results.
35 students chose blue.

What angle will the sector for blue be on Bertie's pie chart?

- A 35°
- B 105°
- C 90°
- D 126°

✓ ✗ Revise page 118

63 Scatter graphs

Describe the relationship shown on this scatter graph.

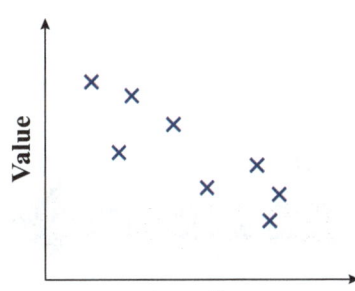

- A Exponential decay
- B Positive correlation
- C Direct proportion
- D Negative correlation

✓ ✗ Revise page 119

64 Averages and range

The stem-and-leaf diagram shows the weights of 10 satsumas.

6	4 9
7	0 1 5 5 6 9
8	2 4 7 7 7 8 8
9	0 1 3 6

Key: 6 | 4 means 64 grams

Work out the mean of the weights.

- A 76.1 g
- B 23 g
- C 75 g
- D 5.1 g

✓ ✗ Revise pages 120, 124

Knowledge check

65 Averages from tables

The table shows the number of goals scored by a team in 40 matches.

Goals	0	1	2	3	4
Frequency	11	15	8	5	1

Work out the mean number of goals scored per match.

- A 2 goals
- B 8 goals
- C 1.25 goals
- D 2.5 goals

Revise pages 121, 122

66 Collecting data

Which of the following **does not** describe a random sample?

- A Writing names in alphabetical order and choosing the first ten names
- B Assigning a number to each person and using a random number generator
- C Choosing names out of a hat
- D Asking each person to flip a coin and selecting anyone who gets heads

Revise page 125

67 Basic probability

A fair six-sided dice is rolled.

Work out the probability of landing on an even number.

- A 3
- B $\frac{1}{6}$
- C $\frac{1}{2}$
- D 0.3

Revise page 127

Answers to the Knowledge check are on the back cover (page 20) of this booklet

68 Probability and outcomes

The table shows the probability of each score on a biased dice.

Score	1	2	3	4	5	6
Probability	0.1	0.1	0.1	0.1	x	x

Ravi rolls the dice. Work out the probability that it lands on 6.

- A 0.2
- B 0.3
- C 0.36
- D 1.2

Revise page 128

69 Independent events

A bag contains 7 black counters and 3 white counters.
Jenna chooses a counter at random, then replaces it.
She then picks a second counter at random.
Work out the probability that she picks **two** white counters.

- A $\frac{6}{10}$
- B $\frac{9}{49}$
- C $\frac{6}{20}$
- D $\frac{9}{100}$

Revise pages 129, 130, 133

70 Venn diagrams

A number is chosen at random from this Venn diagram.

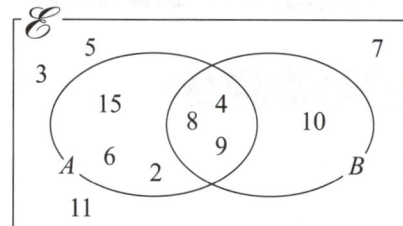

Work out the probability that it is a member of the set $A \cup B$.

- A $\frac{7}{11}$
- B $\frac{3}{11}$
- C $\frac{3}{7}$
- D $\frac{6}{11}$

Revise pages 131, 132

My catch-up plan

Use this page to make your own customised catch-up plan. Write down all the pages that you plan to revise, then use the tick boxes to track your progress.

Page	Had a go	Nearly there	Nailed it!	Page	Had a go	Nearly there	Nailed it!
……	☐	☐	☐	……	☐	☐	☐
……	☐	☐	☐	……	☐	☐	☐
……	☐	☐	☐	……	☐	☐	☐
……	☐	☐	☐	……	☐	☐	☐
……	☐	☐	☐	……	☐	☐	☐
……	☐	☐	☐	……	☐	☐	☐
……	☐	☐	☐	……	☐	☐	☐
……	☐	☐	☐	……	☐	☐	☐
……	☐	☐	☐	……	☐	☐	☐
……	☐	☐	☐	……	☐	☐	☐
……	☐	☐	☐	……	☐	☐	☐
……	☐	☐	☐	……	☐	☐	☐
……	☐	☐	☐	……	☐	☐	☐
……	☐	☐	☐	……	☐	☐	☐
……	☐	☐	☐	……	☐	☐	☐
……	☐	☐	☐	……	☐	☐	☐
……	☐	☐	☐	……	☐	☐	☐
……	☐	☐	☐	……	☐	☐	☐
……	☐	☐	☐	……	☐	☐	☐
……	☐	☐	☐	……	☐	☐	☐
……	☐	☐	☐	……	☐	☐	☐
……	☐	☐	☐	……	☐	☐	☐
……	☐	☐	☐	……	☐	☐	☐
……	☐	☐	☐	……	☐	☐	☐
……	☐	☐	☐	……	☐	☐	☐
……	☐	☐	☐	……	☐	☐	☐
……	☐	☐	☐	……	☐	☐	☐

Notes

Use these pages to make any other catch-up notes you need. You could list topics that you know you need extra help with, or make a note of any facts or definitions you are struggling to remember. Or you could use them to record dates and times of catch-up sessions, extra tutorials or study periods.

GCSE MATHEMATICS FOUNDATION
CATCH-UP 2020

Matching chart

You can use this chart to help you choose pages for your catch-up plan. Tick the units and topics you want to revise, and then add the pages listed to your plan on page 15.

Unit / topic	Revision Guide / Workbook pages	Revise? ✓
Unit 1: Number		☐
Integers and place value	1, 2, 4, 5, 16	☐
Decimals	3, 6, 7, 10	☐
Indices, powers and roots	8, 9	☐
Factors, multiples and primes	11, 12, 13	☐
Unit 2: Algebra		☐
Algebra: the basics	22, 23, 24, 25	☐
Expanding and factorising single brackets	28, 29	☐
Expressions and substitution into formulae	25, 26, 27	☐
Unit 3: Graphs, tables and charts		☐
Tables	77, 115, 121, 122	☐
Charts and graphs	116, 117, 123, 124	☐
Pie charts	118	☐
Scatter graphs	119	☐
Unit 4: Fractions and percentages		☐
Fractions	13, 14	☐
Fractions, decimals and percentages	55, 56	☐
Percentages	55, 57, 58	☐
Unit 5: Equations, inequalities and sequences		✓
Equations	30, 31, 51	☐
Inequalities	32, 33	☐
Sequences	34, 35	☐
Unit 6: Angles		☐
Properties of shapes, parallel lines and angle facts	71, 72, 73, 74, 75, 95	☐
Interior and exterior angles of polygons	76	☐
Unit 7: Averages and range		☐
Statistics and sampling	125	☐
The averages	120, 121, 122, 126	☐

GCSE MATHEMATICS FOUNDATION CATCH-UP 2020

If your school follows the Pearson Edexcel two- or three-year scheme of work, you can use the shading on the left-hand side of the table to help you find the topics you are most likely to have missed between spring half term and the summer holiday. You can also check with your teacher to find out exactly which topics you should have covered during lockdown.

Unit / topic	Revision Guide / Workbook pages	Revise? ✓
Unit 8: Perimeter, area and volume 1		☐
Perimeter and area	61, 79, 80, 81, 84, 85	☐
3D forms and volume	82, 83, 84, 85	☐
Unit 9: Graphs		☐
Real-life graphs	37, 40, 41, 42	☐
Straight-line graphs	36, 37, 38, 39	☐
Unit 10: Transformations	86, 87, 88, 89	☐
Unit 11: Ratio and proportion	59, 60, 67, 68	☐
Unit 12: Right-angled triangles		☐
Pythagoras' theorem	90, 91	☐
Trigonometry	92, 93, 94	☐
Unit 13: Probability		☐
Probability and counting	19, 127, 128, 129	☐
Representing probabilities and outcomes	130, 131, 132, 133	☐
Unit 14: Multiplicative reasoning		☐
More percentages	62, 63	☐
Rates of change and compound measures	64, 65, 66, 68	☐
Unit 15: Constructions, loci and bearings		☐
Plans and elevations	82, 95, 96, 97	☐
Constructions, loci and bearings	98, 99, 100, 101, 102	☐
Unit 16: Quadratic equations and graphs		☐
Quadratic equations: expanding and factorising	43, 46, 47	☐
Quadratic graphs	44, 45	☐
Unit 17: Perimeter, area and volume 2		☐
Circles	103, 104, 105	☐
Cylinders, cones and spheres	106, 107, 108	☐
Unit 18: Fractions, indices, standard form	15, 17, 18	☐
Unit 19: Congruence, similarity, vectors	109, 110, 111, 112	☐
Unit 20: More algebra	48, 49, 50, 51, 52	☐

Two-year scheme of work units
Three-year scheme of work units

Knowledge check answers

1	B	2	A	3	D	4	D	5	B
6	A	7	B	8	C	9	C	10	A
11	C	12	A	13	D	14	D	15	B
16	B	17	B	18	D	19	D	20	A
21	D	22	B	23	B	24	A	25	C
26	A	27	C	28	C	29	B	30	A
31	D	32	C	33	C	34	B	35	A
36	A	37	A	38	D	39	D	40	C
41	B	42	C	43	D	44	A	45	C
46	C	47	C	48	D	49	B	50	D
51	A	52	C	53	C	54	B	55	C
56	B	57	D	58	A	59	D	60	B
61	A	62	D	63	D	64	A	65	C
66	A	67	C	68	B	69	D	70	A

Published by Pearson Education Limited, 80 Strand, London, WC2R 0RL.

www.pearsonschoolsandfecolleges.co.uk

Copies of official specifications for all Pearson qualifications may be found on the website: qualifications.pearson.com

Text and illustrations © Pearson Education Ltd 2020
Produced, typeset and illustrated by
Florence Production Ltd, Stoodleigh, Devon UK

Cover illustration thumbnails by Pearson Education Ltd

The right of Harry Smith to be identified as author of this work has been asserted by him in accordance with the Copyright, Designs and Patents Act 1988.

First published 2020
23 22 21
10 9 8 7 6 5 4 3

British Library Cataloguing in Publication Data
A catalogue record for this book is available from the British Library

ISBN 9781292374826

Copyright notice
All rights reserved. No part of this publication may be reproduced in any form or by any means (including photocopying or storing it in any medium by electronic means and whether or not transiently or incidentally to some other use of this publication) without the written permission of the copyright owner, except in accordance with the provisions of the Copyright, Designs and Patents Act 1988 or under the terms of a licence issued by the Copyright Licensing Agency, 5th Floor, Shackleton House, Hay's Galleria, 4 Battle Bridge Lane, London, SE1 2HX (www.cla.co.uk). Applications for the copyright owner's written permission should be addressed to the publisher.

Printed in the UK by Ashford Colour Press

Notes from the publisher
1. While the publishers have made every attempt to ensure that advice on the qualification and its assessment is accurate, the official specification and associated assessment guidance materials are the only authoritative source of information and should always be referred to for definitive guidance.

Pearson examiners have not contributed to any sections in this resource relevant to examination papers for which they have responsibility.

2. Pearson has robust editorial processes, including answer and fact checks, to ensure the accuracy of the content in this publication, and every effort is made to ensure this publication is free of errors. We are, however, only human, and occasionally errors do occur. Pearson is not liable for any misunderstandings that arise as a result of errors in this publication, but it is our priority to ensure that the content is accurate. If you spot an error, please do contact us at resourcescorrections@pearson.com so we can make sure it is corrected.